Round the year with Rosie & Jim

Stories ★ Poems ★ Puzzles ★ Activities

Scholastic Children's Books,
Scholastic Publications Ltd,
7–9 Pratt Street, London NW1 0AE, UK

Scholastic Inc.
730 Broadway, New York, NY 10003, USA

Scholastic Canada Ltd,
123 Newkirk Road, Richmond Hill,
Ontario, Canada L4C 3G5

Ashton Scholastic Pty Ltd,
PO Box 579, Gosford, New South Wales,
Australia

Ashton Scholastic Ltd,
Private Bag 1, Penrose, Auckland 6,
New Zealand

10 9 8 7 6 5 4 3 2 1

ISBN 0 590 54058 0

Made and printed by Proost International Book production, Belgium.
Typeset by Goodfellow & Egan.

Round the year with Rosie & Jim
Autumn and Winter

by John Cunliffe and Anita Ganeri
Illustrated by Joan Hickson

A Ragdoll Production for Central Independent Television

André Deutsch Children's Books
Scholastic Children's Books
London

Autumn and Winter

Autumn and Winter have come round again. Rosie and Jim have to wrap up warm. But there is plenty to look at as they sail along on the *Ragdoll*.

Here is a tree in Autumn.
Can you find these four things
in the picture?

Squirrel   Mushrooms
Spider   Deer

Here is a tree in Winter.
Can you find these four things
in the picture?

Robin   Snowdrops
Snowman   Holly

Autumn and Winter on the Waterways

This is a quiet time on the rivers and canals. The holiday-makers have gone home, and many of the boats are locked up at their winter moorings. Some canals are closed so that repairs can be made to the lock-gates. Some parts of the canal are even drained of water so that work can be done on the bottom of the canal.

When it is very cold, the canals sometimes become covered in ice. Then, no boats can move. They are all stuck fast. The people who live in their boats must keep a good store of wood or coal for the stove. They must close all hatches tightly, and stay cosy and warm in the cabin. There are plenty of jobs to be done inside: brasses to be polished, and engines and ropes to be mended.

The *Ragdoll* is moored quite close to a village in the winter, and Rosie and Jim can hear carol singing in the village church at Christmas time. Across the field there's a shallow pond where people love to skate. No-one skates on the canal because it's much too dangerous.

In Winter, many of the birds fly away to warmer lands. Crumbs and scraps thrown out each morning are very welcome to birds that stay. Blue Tits feed from a bag of nuts hung on the washing line. Every morning John breaks the ice with a boat-hook so that the birds can get a drink.

A Game of Football

Rosie and Jim were sailing along on the *Ragdoll*.

"I'm cold," said Jim.

"Well, noggin," said Rosie, "that's because it's Autumn."

"What's that?" said Jim.

"Ooh, noodle," said Rosie. "Don't you know? Spring and Summer are warm and Autumn and Winter are cold. It's . . . well, it's just the time of year."

"It's two o'clock," said Jim.

"Gobbin," said Rosie, "not that sort of time. Umm . . . October, November, . . . that sort of time."

"Oh," said Jim.

"You know," said Rosie. "When the leaves drop off the trees and we stay inside by the fire."

"Yes," said Jim. "But I'm still cold."

"What about fizzgog, steering the boat?" said Rosie.

"Poor old fizzgog, he must be freezing," said Jim.

"I know how to get warm," said Rosie.

"Put more wood on the stove," said Jim.

"No, silly," said Rosie. "We'll play a game to warm us up."

"What?" said Jim.

"Wait and see," said Rosie.

They heard Duck quacking, and John came into the cabin to get his shopping-bag. Rosie and Jim sat still and pretended to be dolls. As soon as John had gone, and Duck had quacked again, Rosie nudged Jim in the ribs, winked, and said, "Come on, Jim."

"Where are we going, Rosie?" said Jim.

"We're going to have a game of football," said Rosie.

She found a ball in John's cupboard, and off they went.

The boat was moored near to a wide piece of grass.

"Here's a good place to play," said Rosie.

Some children had been playing there, and they had marked goals with piles of stones.

7

"You're in goal, Jim," said Rosie, "and you have to stop me scoring."

They had great fun, and they soon got really warm. Then Rosie kicked the ball so hard that it went high up above Jim's goal and dropped into the middle of someone's garden.

Just then John came back! Rosie and Jim quickly jumped into the boat, and sat still on their seat.

"Is this your ball?" said the lady in the garden, giving John a funny look. Perhaps she thought he was too old to be playing football?

"Er . . . yes," said John. "Thank you. I wonder how it got into your garden?"

John put the ball on the roof of the boat and went to put his shopping away.

"Come on, Jim," said Rosie. "It's my turn in goal."

This time they played well away from the lady's garden. But then Jim kicked the ball high in the air, and it landed in the middle of the canal!

"Oh dear," said Rosie, "now we've done it. We'll never get it back!"

But a man came along with his dog. When he saw the ball in the middle of the water, he shouted, "*Fetch!*" to the dog. It jumped in, and brought the ball back in its mouth. Just then John came out of the cabin. Rosie and Jim hid behind a bush.

"Is this your ball?" said the man.

"Oh . . . yes," said John. "I wonder how it got into the canal? I left it on the roof of the boat. Thank you very much."

The man gave John a very funny look.

"It's these children, you know," he said. "They never think."

"No," said John, "I suppose they don't."

He wondered which children the man was talking about. He didn't hear Rosie and Jim giggling and nudging each other in the cabin of his boat.

John left the ball in a bucket on the front of the boat, and went off to get his tea.

"It'll never escape from there," he said.

But Rosie and Jim slipped out whilst John was watching television, and took the ball out of the bucket and along the canal bank for another game.

This time they climbed up the hill over the tunnel, and played at kicking the ball to each other in the long grass. They had a lovely time, and felt as warm as a summer's day. Until . . . until Rosie kicked the ball, and Jim missed it, and the ball just disappeared.

"Where is it?" said Rosie.

"It's gone," said Jim.

"Look!" said Rosie.

There was a deep hole going down into the ground, with a wall around it, like a well.

"I know what it is," said Jim.

"It's a big hole," said Rosie.

"That lets air into the tunnel that goes under the hill," said Jim.

"That's it," said Rosie.

"And John's ball has gone down it," said Jim.

"And we'll never be able to find it now," said Rosie.

"Oh dear," said Jim, "what will John say?"

Rosie and Jim walked back to the boat. They heard Duck quacking and hid before John saw them. He was on deck looking in his bucket. "Bless me!" he said. "That ball's gone again!"

Just then, a boat came through the tunnel under the hill. In its chimney was the ball.

"Is this your ball?" said the girl steering the boat.

"Well, yes, it is," said John. "But I've no idea how it got into your chimney."

"I think I know," said the girl. "But I can't tell you."

She had seen Rosie and Jim running to hide, and she knew the tricks they could get up to. But grown-ups never see Rosie and Jim coming to life, so she thought John might not believe her if she told him. Besides, she wanted to keep Rosie and Jim's secret.

"Well," said John. "I'd better be on my way now, before any more odd things happen. Cheerio!"

Rosie and Jim slipped into the boat, and sat still, pretending to be dolls again. John popped his ball into a cupboard, untied the rope, and went on his way.

Activity Game

Make a football game

Here's a game to play on an Autumn night, when it's too cold and dark to go outside.

What you will need:

2 shoeboxes (without lids) ● drinking straws ● a ping-pong ball (or a piece of paper scrunched up into a ball)

You can play this game with two people or in two teams of two.

What you have to do:

1. Play this game on a large table or on the floor. Set up the shoeboxes, as shown. These are the goalposts.

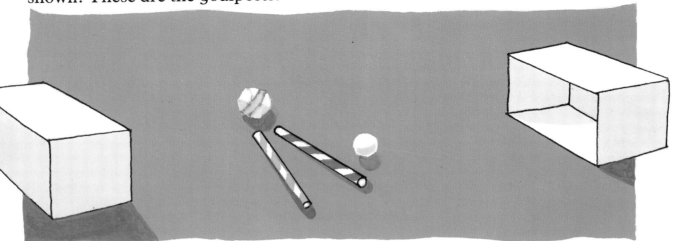

2. Put the ball in the middle of the pitch. Each person should take a straw and start blowing through it to make the ball move.

3. The aim of the game is to blow the ball into the opposite goal. You mustn't touch the ball with the straw or your hands.

The Rosie and Jim Song

Both sing:
Rosie and Jim,
Rosie and Jim,
Chugging along
On the old Ragdoll;
Rosie and Jim,
Rosie and Jim,
and John . . .
He steers the boat.

●

We go to play
And have a look;
With Rosie's bag,

Jim sings:
And my drawing book

Both sing:
The world drifts by
The window-frame,
And Rosie and Jim
We play our games.

●

Rosie and Jim,
Rosie and Jim,
Finding stories every day,
Rosie and Jim,
Rosie and Jim,
And John he writes them down.

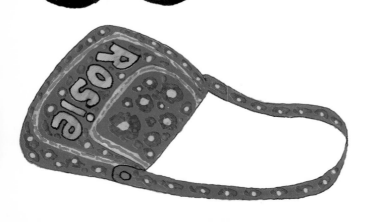

Autumn Diary   October

Fri   There was such a wind last night! I thought it was going to blow The Ragdoll right out of the water! When I looked out this morning, a huge tree had fallen across the canal. A traffic jam of boats was waiting to get past.

Sat   A huge crane arrived today to try to move the tree. A man with a power saw chopped the tree up first. He cut right through it! I could see the pattern of rings that tells you how old a tree is. There were so many rings I couldn't count them all. It must be hundreds of years old!

Sun   I went for a walk swishing through the leaves on the canal banks. There are all sorts of trees there. My favourites are the silver birches. The fallen tree has been cleared away at last. I made a fire with some of the wood from its branches.

OAK   HORSE CHESTNUT   ASH   APPLE

Making Autumn Trees

In Autumn, the leaves on the trees change colour. They turn gold, red and brown before they fall off in Winter. Rosie and Jim like to make their own Autumn trees. You could make one, too.

What you will need:

newspapers ● sticky tape ● cardboard tubes from the middle of toilet rolls ● paper for leaves ● paint and paintbrush ● scissors

Ask a grown up to help you with the cutting out.

What you have to do:

1. Cut up a newspaper like this. Don't cut right through to the other side.

2. Roll the newspaper up, quite tightly. Tape the ends to keep them in place.

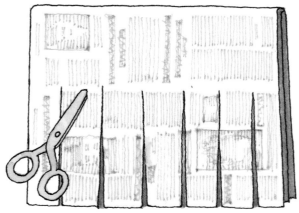

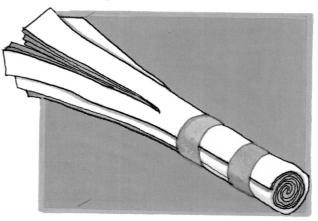

3. Gently, pull the paper from the centre to make your tree's branches. The more you pull, the taller your tree will grow.

4. Make a tree trunk from a cardboard tube. Cut slits in the bottom. Fold them out to make a firm base. Then slip your paper tree inside.

5. Decorate your tree with green and brown paint. You could add leaves painted with Autumn colours. Stick them on with tape. Why not collect some fallen leaves and stick those on, too?

Seeing spots

Many animals hibernate in Autumn. They go to sleep until the warm Spring weather comes. Ladybirds hibernate too, under leaves and on plant stems. They sleep all huddled together, like the ones here. Can you count them all? How many spots does each one have?

Next time you see a ladybird, remember to count its spots!

Bedtime

Jim looked out of the window. "Rosie," he said. "It's only tea-time and it's nearly dark."

"Ooh, noggin," said Rosie, "that's because it's Winter."

"Will it get darker and darker?" said Jim.

"Course it will," said Rosie.

"Until it's dark all day?"

"Ooh no, gobbin. Summer will come back, and it'll be sunny till after John's bedtime. But it's our bedtime now, so we'd better tidy up and get our supper before John sees all this mess."

"Rosie?"

"Yes, Jim."

"Can we play just a little bit longer?"

"No, Jim, it's bed-time. Duck's quacking his sleepy song, and if John sees us . . ."

"He's busy writing his story, Rosie, he won't notice a thing for hours and hours."

"Jim!"

Rosie was getting cross.

"Yes, Rosie."

Jim began, very slowly, to put away the crayons, felt-tip pens, paper, scissors, glue and paints that he had been playing with. Rosie didn't see how Jim tidied things. He just opened a drawer and stuffed everything

in, all in a jumble. Rosie tidied her books away neatly. Then they quietly got their supper, snuggled up on their settee, and closed their eyes.

Soon, a little voice came out of the darkness. "Rosie?"

"What?"

"Can I have a drink of water?"

"Oh, Jim, I thought you were asleep ages ago."

"Just a *little* drink?"

"Well . . . be quick and don't let John hear you."

But John did hear Jim getting a drink of water. He came to look.

"I'm sure I heard something," said John. "I wonder if there are some mice living on my boat?"

Jim shut his eyes and pretended to be asleep, just in time.

John scratched his head. Then he went to the drawer to get a felt-tip pen. He opened the drawer, and all the things that Jim had stuffed in, in such a jumble, tumbled out on to the floor.

"Oh dear, what a mess!" said John. "What a mess. I really must tidy this drawer. I wonder how it's got like this?"

He turned the drawer upside down, tipping everything on to the floor. Then he found the pen he wanted.

"That mess will have to wait," he said. "I must get back to my story."

All was dark and still. But then a little voice came out of the darkness. "Rosie?"

"What is it now?" said Rosie, getting crosser.

"I'm not sleepy. Can I play just a little bit more?"

"Yes," said Rosie.

"Really?" said Jim, very surprised. "Can I?"

"You can play at tidying that drawer properly," said Rosie.

"Oh, Rosie, I didn't mean that!"

"I do," said Rosie.

So Jim had to tidy everything in John's drawer.

An owl flew past the window, then hooted from the tree. "He doesn't have to go to sleep," said Jim.

"He's a night creature," said Rosie. "He sleeps all day, instead."

"Can't I be a night creature?" said Jim.

"No," said Rosie, "you're all right as you are."

A hedgehog went snuffling by in the hedge. "There goes another night creature," said Rosie. "Have you finished that drawer?"

"Yes," said Jim.

"Let me see," said Rosie. "Lovely, now you can go to sleep."

And Jim was so tired with tidying John's drawer, that he did!

The next day, when John looked in his drawer, what a lovely surprise he had.

"I don't remember tidying this drawer," he said. "They must be very clever mice that live on my boat. Very clever indeed."

Jim smiled, and Rosie gave him a nudge in the ribs. But they didn't say a word.

Puzzle Page

Follow the tracks

There are lots of animal tracks in this newly-fallen snow. Can you trace each track back to its owner?

Things to do

Shadow play

In Autumn and Winter, it gets dark very quickly. John is walking back to the *Ragdoll*. The moon is out and there are lots of spooky shadows. Can you see who they belong to?

Hide and seek

John is playing hide and seek with Rosie and Jim. It's their turn to hide. He can't find Rosie and Jim anywhere. Can you?

Winter Diary   December

Sat   It was very still and quiet when I woke up. I couldn't even hear the water lapping. I looked out of the window. The canal was frozen solid! The trees looked lovely with frost on their branches, but the ducks and sparrows were cold and hungry. I filled the breakfast tablecloth with scraps of bread and crumbs and scattered them on the ice for the birds to eat.

Sun   It started to snow this morning. I stayed in and stoked up the stove to keep warm. It was a good day to write my Christmas cards. I decided to make my own. I made some lovely leafy prints.

Mon   Today was the last day for posting Christmas cards, so I rushed to the post office. I got there in plenty of time. They even let me look around the sorting office.

Tues Too cold to go outside today. I thought I'd write a story about the post office instead. I'm glad I'm not a postman this winter!

MALLARD

TUFTED

POCHARD

PINTAIL

Sleepy Song

Rosie and Jim sing this song to help them fall asleep.

Rock-a-bye sleepy,
I-n a boat,
It's nice to sleep,
When you're afloat;

Rocking on
The gentle streams,
Cosy nights,
And . . . sweet dreams.

Christmas Post

Rosie and Jim make their own Christmas cards. You can try making your own too. Here's what you have to do.

What you will need:
thin card ● paints or crayons ● sticky paper ● scissors

What you have to do:
1. Ask a grown-up to help cut the card into an oblong shape.

2. Draw a Christmas picture on one side of the card.

3. Fold the card in half so the picture is on the inside. On the outside write your Christmas message on the left and the address on the right.

4. Cut out some stamps from the sticky paper. These could be in the shape of Christmas trees or stars. Stick them on each card.

Now you need somewhere to post your cards. Try making your own bright red postbox.

What you will need:
an old shoebox • some red paint • scissors

What you have to do:

1. Ask a grown-up to cut a slit in the lid wide enough for a card to fit through.

2. Paint the box and lid red.

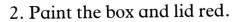

3. Stand the box on its end and post your cards!

Rosie and Jim's Christmas Party

It was a cold and wintery day. Jim looked out of the window, and said, "Rosie, look! Look in the windows of the houses. They all have pretty green trees in them."

"Trees?" said Rosie. "Ooh, noggin, trees don't grow in houses."

"They do today," said Jim. "And they all have lights on them."

"Lights on trees?" said Rosie. "Let me see."

Sure enough there were decorated trees, one in every house they passed, brightly lit in the dusk. What a puzzle for two ragdolls, who had never seen such a thing before! They found the answer when a little girl came walking along the canal path, with her mother. Rosie and Jim called to her.

"Yoo-hoo! Hello little girl!"

Her mother stopped to chat with John. And, whilst the grown-ups talked, the little girl looked in at the open window and talked to Rosie and Jim. The little girl was called Carla, and it wasn't long before Jim asked her about the mysterious trees in the houses.

"Don't you know?" said Carla. "It's Christmas."

"Christmas?" said Jim.

"Christmas?" said Rosie. "What's that?"

Carla told them all about Christmas.

"How lovely," said Jim. "We've never seen a Christmas before."

"We must have one," said Rosie.

"With a tree," said Jim.

"And a party," said Rosie. "Will you come to our party, Carla?"

"Yes, please," said Carla.

Then they heard what John was saying to Carla's mother.

"I don't think there'll be any Christmas for me," he said. "The canal's closed further along because of ice, and I won't be able to get to my house, where I keep the boat for the Winter. That's where all my friends live. I expect they'll be having a party. I hope they save some pudding for me."

"Poor old fizzgog," said Rosie.

"No Christmas for fuzzy-face," said Jim, sadly.

"Why don't you . . ." said Carla, " . . .and I'll . . ." she whispered in Rosie's ear, so that Jim couldn't hear.

"Ooh, yes," said Rosie, "what a fizzy idea. And all your friends? Lovely."

"What did she say?" said Jim, when Carla had walked off with her mother.

Suddenly Duck quacked, to warn them that John was coming into the cabin, so she didn't tell him just then. But Jim soon found out what it was.

Later that day, when John had settled down in his chair for a sleep, Rosie and Jim crept out and jumped ashore. There was a wood by the river, where there were hundreds of fir trees. Rosie had found some tinsel and baubles in the drawer, and they fixed them in the branches of a small fir tree, near to the boat. Then Jim said, "Look, Rosie!"

There was a whole crowd of children, with their mothers and fathers, coming along the path by the water. They made a circle round Rosie and Jim's Christmas tree, and began to sing, "Good King Wenceslas." John woke up and rubbed his eyes. Then he looked out. What a surprise he had! He called out, "Merry Christmas!" to them all.

And they all came aboard the *Ragdoll* with the presents they had brought for John; good things to eat, and all kinds of things to make his Christmas a happy one. They had a lovely party on board the boat. Then they all asked John to visit their homes for their Christmas parties.

Rosie and Jim's eyes twinkled as John said, "This is the best Christmas *ever*!"

More Winter Fun

Make a Winter mobile

This Winter mobile makes a good decoration for your room at Christmas time. It is easy to make!

What you will need:
twig or coat hanger ● tinsel ● different lengths of cotton thread ● sticky tape ● pine cones ● leaves ● Christmas baubles ● cotton wool balls ● and anything wintery.

What you have to do:

1. Wind some tinsel around the twig and tape it in place. You can use the coat hanger instead of the twig.

2. Tie a piece of thread to each cone, leaf or decoration. Add cotton wool balls for snow.

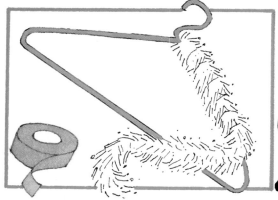 

3. Tape or tie the threads to the twig or hanger. Make sure each side is evenly balanced so your mobile doesn't tilt.

4. Tape another piece of thread to the middle of the twig or hanger. Hang your mobile up.

Spot the difference
Can you spot eleven differences between these two Christmas pictures?

A Walk in Winter

Play this game with Rosie and Jim as they walk through the countryside on the way back to the *Ragdoll*.

You will need a die to throw and a counter for each player. Put all the counters on *START*. Take it in turns to throw the die and move your counter around the board. The first person to reach the *Ragdoll* is the winner.

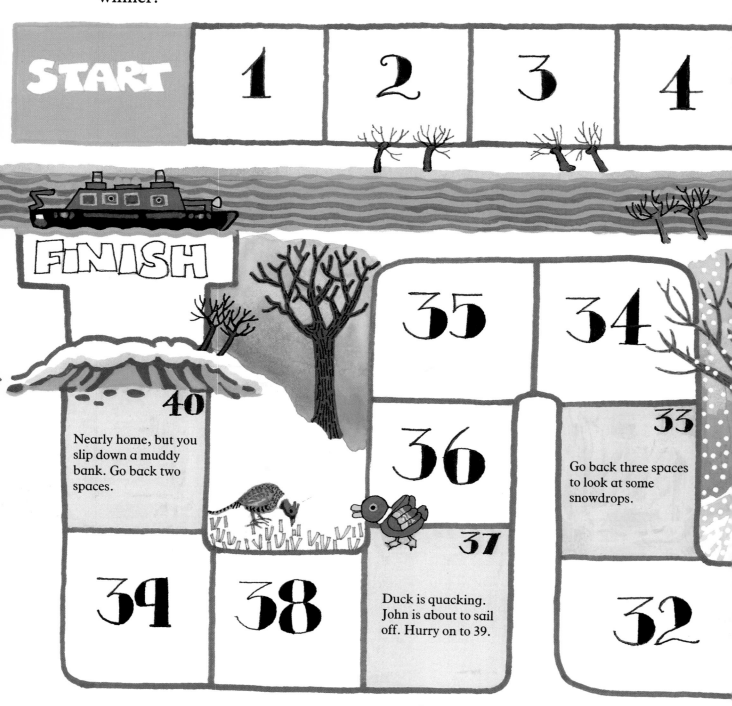

START

1 2 3 4

FINISH

35 34

40 33

Nearly home, but you slip down a muddy bank. Go back two spaces.

36

Go back three spaces to look at some snowdrops.

37

39 38

Duck is quacking. John is about to sail off. Hurry on to 39.

32

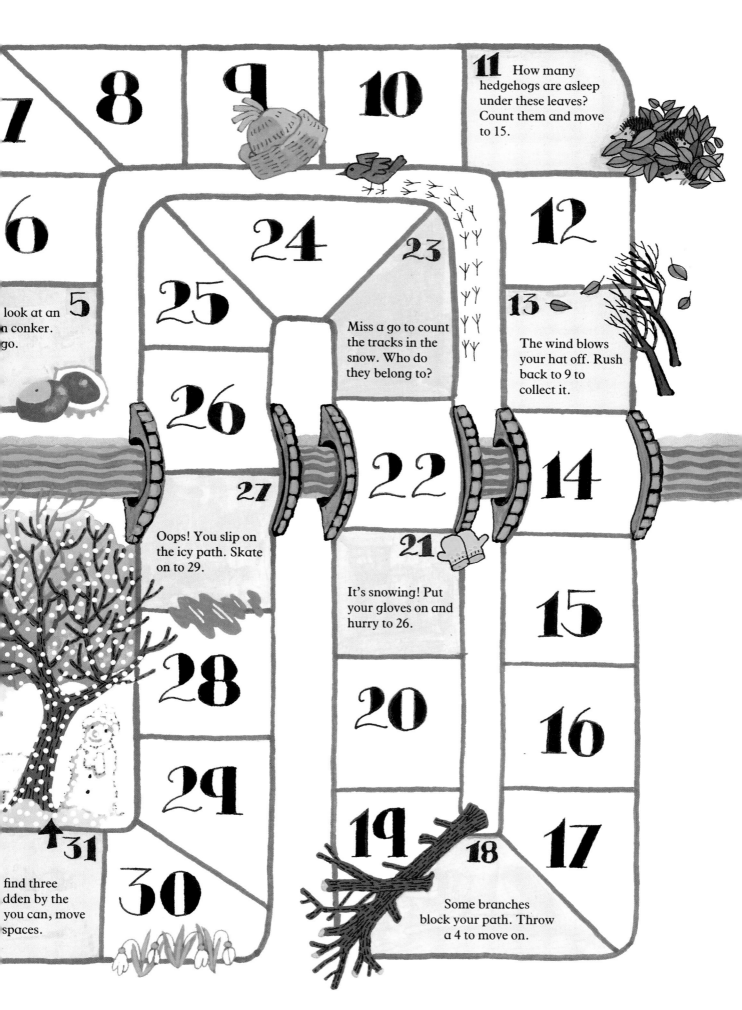

7

8

9

10

11 How many hedgehogs are asleep under these leaves? Count them and move to 15.

6

24

23

12

look at an
conker.
go.

5

25

Miss a go to count the tracks in the snow. Who do they belong to?

13

The wind blows your hat off. Rush back to 9 to collect it.

26

27

22

14

Oops! You slip on the icy path. Skate on to 29.

21

It's snowing! Put your gloves on and hurry to 26.

15

28

20

16

29

19

18

17

31

find three
dden by the
you can, move
spaces.

30

Some branches block your path. Throw a 4 to move on.

Answers

Page 15
There are 14 ladybirds altogether.
They each have 7 spots.

Page 19
Track 1 goes to the bird.
Track 2 goes to the rabbit.
Track 3 goes to the dog.
Track 4 goes to the cat.

Page 20
The shadows are Duck, Jim,
Rosie and John. There's an owl
sitting on the wall, too!

Page 21
Rosie is in the tree, Jim is under
the leaves.

Page 29

Spring and Summer

Spring and Summer

Spring and Summer

Spring and Summer are happy times along the canal. There is plenty for Rosie and Jim to look at as they sail along in the *Ragdoll*.

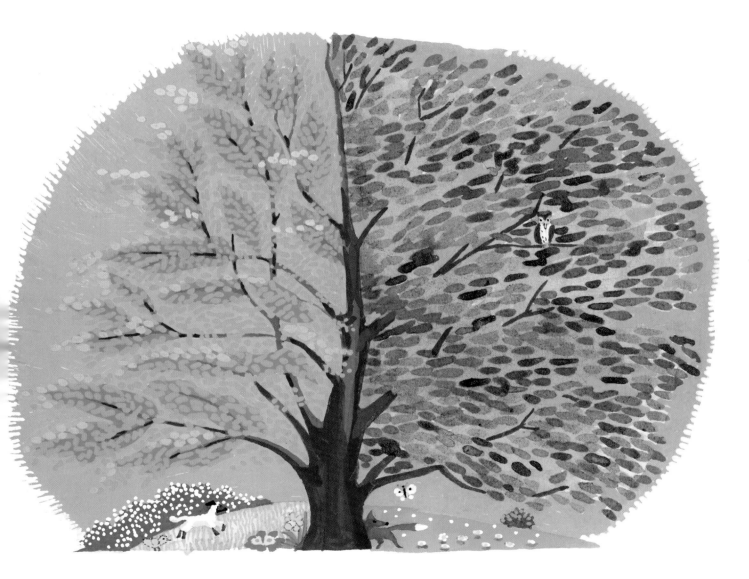

Here is a tree in Spring.
Can you find these four things
in the picture?

Primroses   Daffodil
Chick   Spring lamb

Here is a tree in Summer.
Can you find these four things
in the picture?

Daisies   Butterfly
Owl   Fox

Spring and Summer on the Waterways

In Spring the waterways come to life again after the Winter. Birds begin building their nests for their eggs to hatch. All day they fly and swoop just over the water, catching insects. There are families of young ducks, tiny bundles of fluffy feathers bobbing about on the water.

There are other creatures busy along the banks of the river, too. Moles are burrowing in the field next to the *Ragdoll*, and John can hear the water-voles plopping into the water from their holes in the river-bank. The fish are busy, too, under the water, with their young ones. Sometimes they jump out of the water to catch flies on warm summer days. One day, John saw a seagull swoop down and catch a fish just as it jumped! It scooped the fish up in mid air, and flew off with it. Poor fish!

The boat people too are busy. It's time to open doors and windows to let the fresh Spring air in and set out again along the rivers and canals in search of adventure and new friends. The *Ragdoll* sets out with the rest of them, with John at the helm, on the lookout for new stories.

In the Summer, there is a Waterways Festival. Hundreds of boats gather together, all newly painted and decorated to look their best. There are bands playing, and tents full of good things to eat and drink. There are stalls and displays of boat-painting, rope-plaiting, boat-building, and lots of things to do with boats and water. Old friends meet and all admire each other's boats. People swap stories of their boating adventures.

Sometimes there are days when it is too hot to stay in the boat. John ties up in the shadiest spot he can find, and sits under a tree with a good book. Some days a storm blows up, the rain clouds come rolling over, and Summer rain comes pouring down. John stays snug and dry in the *Ragdoll*. Those are the days he writes his stories.

The Wind Blew

It was a fine Spring morning on the *Ragdoll*. It was a rattly morning as well. There was a shaking and a tapping all over the boat. Jim was frightened. "Rosie," he said, "Rosie, listen! There's somebody knocking!"

Something went tap-tap at the shutter that covered the window.

John got up and came into the cabin to make his coffee. "Hmm," he said, "The wind's getting up."

When he went out on deck, Jim nudged Rosie.

"Did you hear that, Rosie? He says the Wind's getting up."

"Where does it sleep?" said Rosie.

"Let's go and see," said Jim.

They looked all over the boat, but they couldn't find the wind. It wasn't in any of the beds, or under the table, or in the cupboard. Where *could* the wind sleep?

When they went outside, everything was blowing about.

"If this is what happens when the Wind gets up, I wish he would go back to bed," said Rosie.

John thought it would be a good day to do his washing. He went off to the launderette with a big bag of dirty washing.

"That's a good idea," said Rosie. "We'll take ours as well."

So they blew after John, through the windy streets.

They all came back to the boat with their clean washing. John put up a long washing-line, and hung his clothes out to dry. There was plenty of room for Rosie and Jim's washing. John was so busy writing a story, that he didn't notice that there were some very small clothes on his line!

The wind blew and dried their washing.

"Thank you, Wind," said Rosie.

The wind blew even harder, and snatched Jim's shirt off the line.

"Ooh, noggin, Wind," said Jim. "Why did you do that?"

"Poor old Wind's cold," said Rosie, laughing. "He wants to wear your shirt."

Now it lifted the shirt up into the air and blew it into the branches of a tree.

"The tree's wearing my shirt!" said Jim. "I'll never get it, now."

But a boy came along and climbed the tree. He brought Jim's shirt down again.

"Thank you," said Jim. "It didn't fit the tree, anyway."

"Do you want to see my kite?" said the boy.

"Ooh, yes," said Rosie.

"What's a kite?" said Jim.

"Come on, I'll show you," said the boy. "In the park."

John was going for a walk in the park, so Rosie and Jim followed him, and there they saw the boy with his kite. The wind blew the kite high up into the air, and the boy had a big ball of string tied to it. He held the string and the kite pulled and tugged at the string.

"Can I hold it?" said Jim.

So the boy gave Jim a turn.

"I'll help," said Rosie.

But Rosie and Jim were much smaller than the boy. When the wind blew strongly they couldn't hold the kite down. It lifted them off the ground, and they went flying away above the tree-tops.

"We're flying!" shouted Jim.

"Put us down!" shouted Rosie. "We want to go home."

The wind softened, and put them down in a pond full of ducks! Poor old Rosie and Jim! Wasn't it lucky that Duck flew down just then? They climbed on his back, and he paddled to the shore. They went home to the boat dripping, and sat in front of the stove until they were dry.

"I think John would like a kite," said Rosie.

"It wouldn't fly away with him," said Jim, "he's much too heavy."

"Let's make him one," said Rosie.

So they did.

What a surprise John had when he came back to the boat, and found a kite tied to his washing-line, flying high in the sky.

"How lovely! I had a kite like that when I was a boy," said John. "It's just the thing for a windy day. I wonder who's left it for me?"

But he never guessed.

Things to do

Breezy Balloons

Make balloon faces of Rosie and Jim, and see how they fly on a breezy day. Keep tight hold of the string!

What you will need:

2 balloons • felt-tip pens • coloured sticky paper • scissors • red and black wool • ball of string • tape

What you have to do:

1. Blow up each balloon and tie the end tightly. You might need help to do this.

2. Cut long pieces of black wool for Rosie's hair. Cut shorter pieces of red wool for Jim's hair. Stick the hair on firmly with tape.

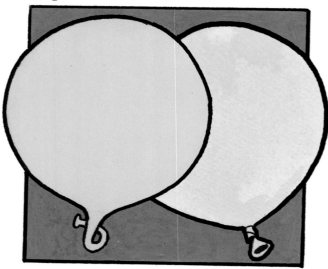

3. Draw shapes on the sticky paper for the cheeks and eyes. Cut them out and stick them on.

4. Use a felt-tip pen to draw their mouths and noses, Rosie's eyelashes and Jim's freckles.

5. Tie a long piece of string to each balloon and let them fly outside in a gentle breeze.

Spot the difference

John has taken two photos of the canal bank in Spring. Rosie and Jim have found nine differences between the two pictures? Can you spot them?

Duck Warnings

John doesn't know that Rosie and Jim come to life. Duck always quacks when John is coming, and Rosie and Jim quickly sing one of these songs.

Ducky's quacking,
Let's disappear;
We mustn't let them,
Spot us here!

Duck is quacking,
Time to go;
Back to the boat,
Before they know!

Ducky's quacking
His quacky song;
Time for home,
We stayed too long!

Spring Diary

April

Tues   Today is the first day of April. It's April Fool's Day. The lock keeper told me the Ragdoll was leaking. I rushed outside to look. It was an April Fool's joke!

Wed   There were lots of baby birds on the canal today. One baby swan was riding on its mother's back. There are ducklings too and baby sparrows in the trees and hedges.

Thurs   I went for a walk across the fields today. There were some young calves running and jumping. They were young bulls! They started to chase me and I had to run for the stile.

Fri   Lots of people came to open up their boats and get them ready for the first trips of the year. I gave the Ragdoll a good polish. My boat looks really smart today!

CHICK

DUCKLING

CYGNET

GOSLING

Baby Animals

Many animals have their babies in Spring. Rosie and Jim are making some newly-hatched Easter chicks in a nest.

What you will need:

yellow wool ● pieces of card ● cotton wool ● small plastic bowl ● brown crêpe paper ● black sticky paper ● scissors

Ask a grown-up to help you with the cutting out.

What you have to do:

1. Cut out two card circles. Use this large circle to trace the shape.

2. Cut out the middle of each circle.

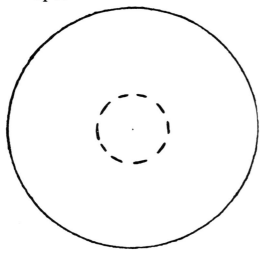

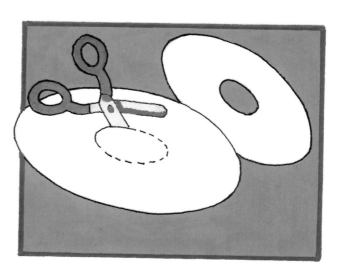

3. Put the two circles together. Then wind the wool round the card until it is completely covered.

4. Cut the wool round the outside edge. Then thread another piece of wool between the two pieces of card.

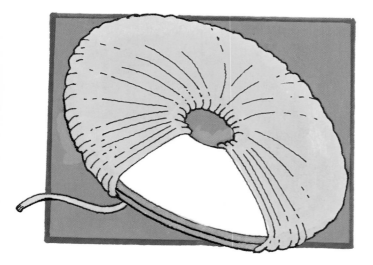

5. Pull it tightly then tie the ends together. Pull the card away. This pom-pom is the chick's body.

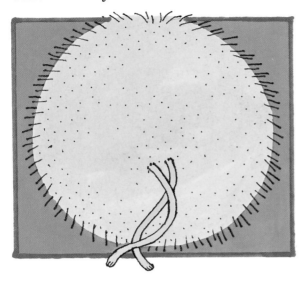

Follow steps 1–5 to make a smaller pom-pom for the chick's head. Use this small circle to trace round.

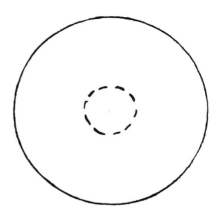

7. Cut a small triangle of card and fold it in half for the beak. Stick it onto the chick's head. Cut out two small circles from the black sticky paper for eyes.

6. Tie the two pom-poms together like this:

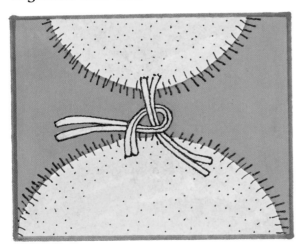

8. Wrap the bowl in brown crêpe paper and fill it with some cosy cotton wool for the nest.

John Keeps Cool!

It was the hottest day of the Summer. It was too hot for John to steer his boat, so he sat under a tree, trying to keep cool. Rosie and Jim sat in the shade of some big leaves. They heard John saying, "It's so hot I could melt! Oh, I do hate being hot. I *wish* I could get cool!"

"Jim," said Rosie, "did you hear that?"

"John's hot," said Jim. "Like us."

"What can we do to cool him down?" said Rosie.

"Water," said Jim. "That makes you cool."

Rosie looked at the canal. "Too dirty for a swim," she said.

"Let's find some clean water," said Jim. "In a pipe."

Rosie and Jim went to look for a pipe. They looked over a fence into a garden, and there was a long green hose-pipe, fastened to a tap. Jim went to get the end of the pipe. Rosie went to turn the tap on. A great fountain of water came spurting out of the pipe, and fell on John – *whooooosh!*

"Oh, help!" shouted John.

"Oh dear," said Rosie.

"Too much water," said Jim.

"But he is cool," said Rosie.

John jumped up to run away from the water, but it seemed to follow him. He jumped into the boat to shelter, and tried to shake himself dry.

"Oh, my book!" he wailed. "It's ruined. A library book, too!"

Rosie and Jim hadn't noticed that John was reading a book under his tree. And now he would be in trouble at the library.

"I'll have to buy them a new book," John said.

He went to find some dry clothes.

"Hmm," he said, "I wonder who squirted that water over me? One thing, it did cool me down. How about a swim? That would be cool. But the canal's much too dirty. I wonder if there's a swimming pool near here? I'll look in my book. A *dry* book! . . . Yes . . . there is . . . not far

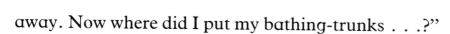

away. Now where did I put my bathing-trunks . . .?"

"What's a swimming pool?" said Jim.

"I don't know," said Rosie. "And what's all this about trunks? Is he taking an elephant with him?"

"We'd better follow and see," said Jim.

When they got to the pool, they saw John jumping into the water. He had taken his clothes off and was wearing a pair of shorts.

"What a funny thing to do," said Rosie.

"He looks very cool," said Jim.

"Let's have a go," said Rosie.

"We'll have to borrow some elephants," said Jim.

"Trunks," said Rosie. "Let's ask this little girl."

"Girls wear a bathing costume," said the little girl, "and mine won't fit you, Rosie. Oh, but my doll's will! Here we are. And here are some trunks to fit Jim."

Rosie and Jim hid their clothes in the little girl's bathing bag and put on the bathing clothes.

"Start in the shallow end," said the little girl, "until you learn to swim."

Rosie and Jim waded into the shallow end. As the water crept up their tummies it tickled them and made them very cold.

"I'll teach you to swim," said the little girl.

Soon, Rosie and Jim were swimming up and down the pool with a crowd of children.

When it was time to go home, Jim said, "I love swimming!"

"It was fizzy," said Rosie.

"And cool," said Jim.

"That was lovely," said John as he sat down at his table. "I think I'll write a cold story, now. Let's see . . . One snowy day . . ."

He didn't notice that Rosie and Jim's hair was still wet, or that Rosie gave Jim a wink before they went to sleep with a smile on their ragdoll faces.

Things to do

A Summer salad

Home-grown cress tastes delicious in summer salads and sandwiches.
Here's how to grow some of your own – it's easy!

What you will need:
cress seeds ● cotton wool ● water ● shallow dish or tray

What you have to do:

1. Line a shallow dish or tray with a layer of cotton wool.

2. Water the cotton wool so it is damp.

3. Sprinkle the cress seeds on top.

4. Keep the dish in a dark, warm place for a few days until the seeds sprout. Cut the cress, wash it, then eat it in a sandwich!

Canal maze

It's a windy day. John is having trouble steering the *Ragdoll*. Can you help him through the maze?

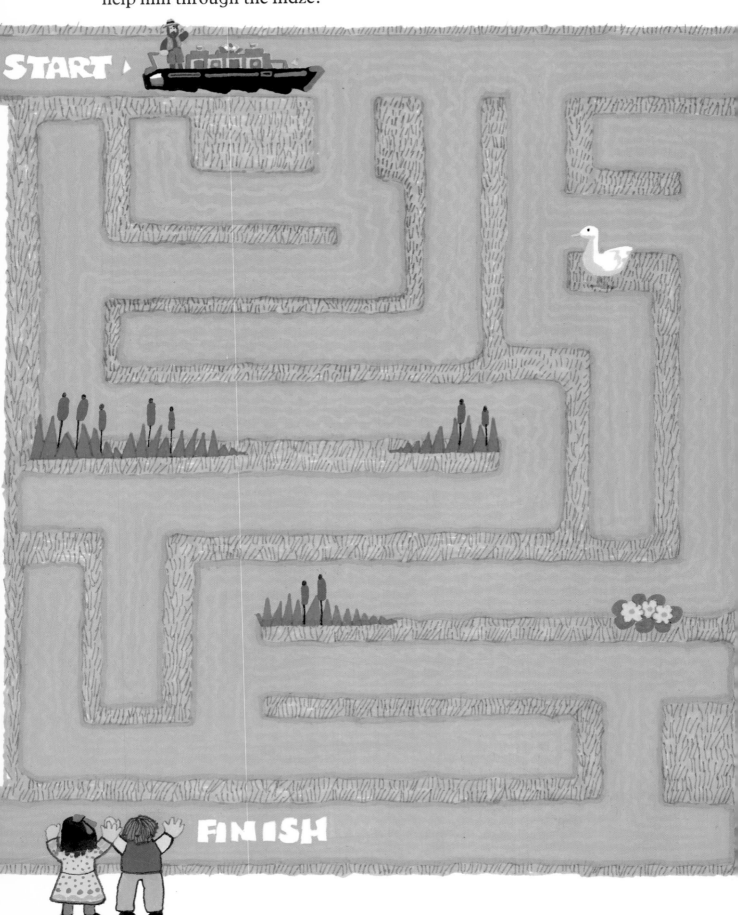

Odd one out

These four butterflies look the same. But one of them is different.
Which one is it?

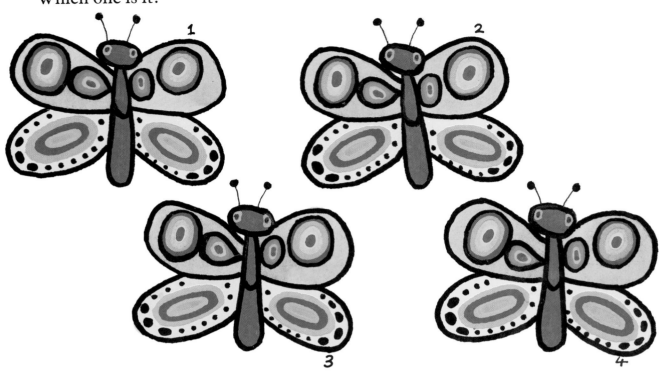

Now, can you spot the odd one out from these four calves?

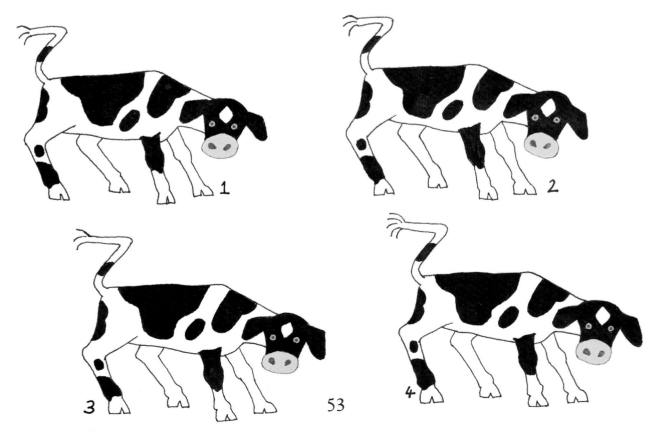

Rosie's Collecting Bag Song

You could find a bag to collect things in, just like Rosie does.

Rosie has a bag,
A collecting bag,
That goes where Rosie goes;
And all the things
That are in her bag,
Well, nobody really knows.

There are tickets and tabs,
And old postcards,
And a piece of Blackpool Rock;
Some chewing-gum,
And a piece of slate,
And a single smelly sock.

There are acorns, conkers,
Twigs and leaves,
And a squashy lump of clay;
Some purple wool,
And a furry mint,
And a piece from a broken tray.

Oh, Rosie has a bag,
A collecting bag,
That goes where Rosie goes;
And all the things
That are in her bag,
Well, nobody really knows.

Thursday 25   July

Mon   It was very hot today! The weather man said it was the hottest day for a hundred years. The only cool place to sit was under a shady tree. I soon fell asleep but I didn't finish my story.

Tues   Today I saw a beautiful butterfly. It was so still that I drew a picture of it. I looked in my water-ways book. There's a butterfly farm nearby! I think I'll sail down there tomorrow.

Wed   Another very hot day, but there was a nice cool breeze when I went down the river on the Ragdoll. I went to the butterfly farm. It was lovely. They had butterflies from all over the world. I bought a picture of one to put in my boat.

BRIMSTONE

CAMBERWELL BEAUTY

RED ADMIRAL

PEACOCK

Butterflies

Make a butterfly

There are lots of butterflies along the canal bank in Summer. Have a go at making some butterflies of your own.

What you will need:

white paper ● thick paint (lots of different colours) ● paintbrush ● sticky tape or glue ● pipe cleaners ● a strip of furry or woolly material ● a thin stick

What you have to do:

1. Fold the white paper in half. Then open it out again.

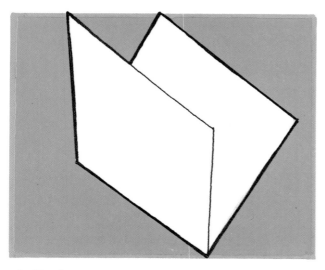

2. With your paintbrush, put two blobs of paint on one side of the paper. Make the top blob bigger than the bottom one. Use different colours for a really bright picture.

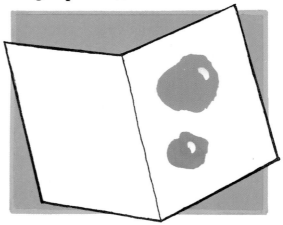

3. Before the paint dries, quickly fold the paper in half again. Press it down with your hand.

4. Open it out and you've got a butterfly. When the paint is dry, cut the butterfly shape out.

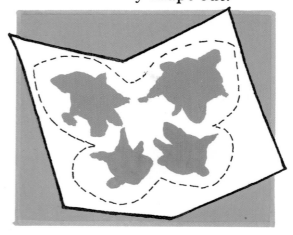

5. Cut a piece of furry or woolly material the length of the butterfly. Glue or tape it on for the body.

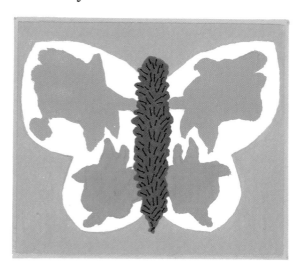

6. Tape two pieces of pipe cleaner to the butterfly's head. These are its feelers.

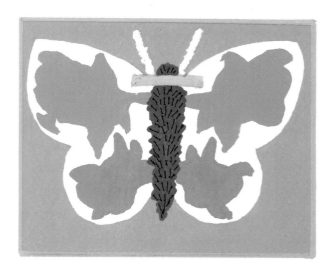

7. Now tape the stick to the back of the butterfly's body. Wave the stick to make the wings fly.

Rosie and Jim's Printing Day

Rosie and Jim loved playing with the things on John's table. There were lots of pens and piles of paper, and they loved to draw pictures and patterns. John often came back and found their pictures.

"Hmm," he would say, "I must have been scribbling whilst I was thinking about a story. But I don't remember drawing *that*!"

One day, they found something else to play with. It had tiny rubber letters on it. "What's this?" said Jim.

"I don't know," said Rosie.

They watched John to see what he did with it. He pressed it on a little cushion, then he pressed it on some paper. "It's made a picture," said Jim.

"Words," said Rosie.

"Magic," said Jim.

When John went out, they had a go.

Jim made the magic words appear on the paper.

Then Rosie pressed her hand on the little cushion.

"Ooh, noggin!" she said, "It's all messy."

She pressed her hand on a piece of paper.

"Look!" said Jim. "It's made a picture of your hand."

"Ooh, fizzy," said Rosie.

"Let me try," said Jim.

Soon, there were hand pictures all over the boat! They drew legs and noses on the hand-shapes, and turned them into elephants, and giraffes, and mice. They scampered and ran all over John's paper!

When John came back, Rosie and Jim sat very still on their seat, and hid their inky hands. What would John say?

"Someone's been playing at printing," he said. "I like their animals. I think some children must have been here, to read my books. That reminds me. I must pop in at the printers to see my new book being printed."

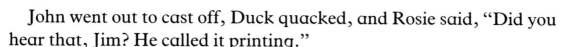

John went out to cast off, Duck quacked, and Rosie said, "Did you hear that, Jim? He called it printing."

"Yes, Rosie. That's what we were doing," said Jim. "And they make John's books like that."

"Not squishing their hands on a messy cushion, noggin!" said Rosie.

"Little words," said Jim.

"Inky words," said Rosie. "Lots of them."

When the boat stopped, they followed John to the printers.

"Look!" said Rosie.

"John's words are on a big roller," said Jim.

"Whizzing round," said Rosie.

"And pictures," said Jim.

"All coloured," said Rosie.

"Magic," said Jim.

"Where's the inky cushion?" said Rosie.

"It's an inky rolling-pin," said Jim, "going whizzy-fizzy."

The words and pictures came out of the printing machine on big sheets of paper. There was a huge pile of them. They saw the paper being folded up and glued to make books.

"What a lot of books!" said Jim.

"For all the children," said Rosie.

John brought some copies of his new book back to the boat.

"I still like these hand-prints," he said. "Thank you, whoever made them."

And he pinned them on the wall by his table.

Rosie and Jim sat very still on their seat, and smiled. And, when John had gone to bed, they read his new book.

More Summer Fun

Animal finger painting

Rosie and Jim love making animal pictures with their fingers. You can try some too. Ask a grown up to help you.

What you will need:

paints ● white paper ● felt-tip pens ● fingers and thumbs!

What you have to do:

1. Before you start, cover the table with newspaper and put on an old shirt.

2. Cover your thumb with paint then press it firmly onto the white paper. This is a rabbit's body.

3. To make the head, dip the tip of your finger into the paint. Press it onto the top of the body.

4. Use felt-tip pens to add ears and a face.

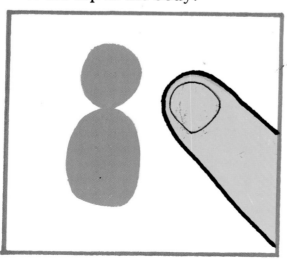

Join the dots

John has lost the *Ragdoll*!
Join the dots to bring it back.

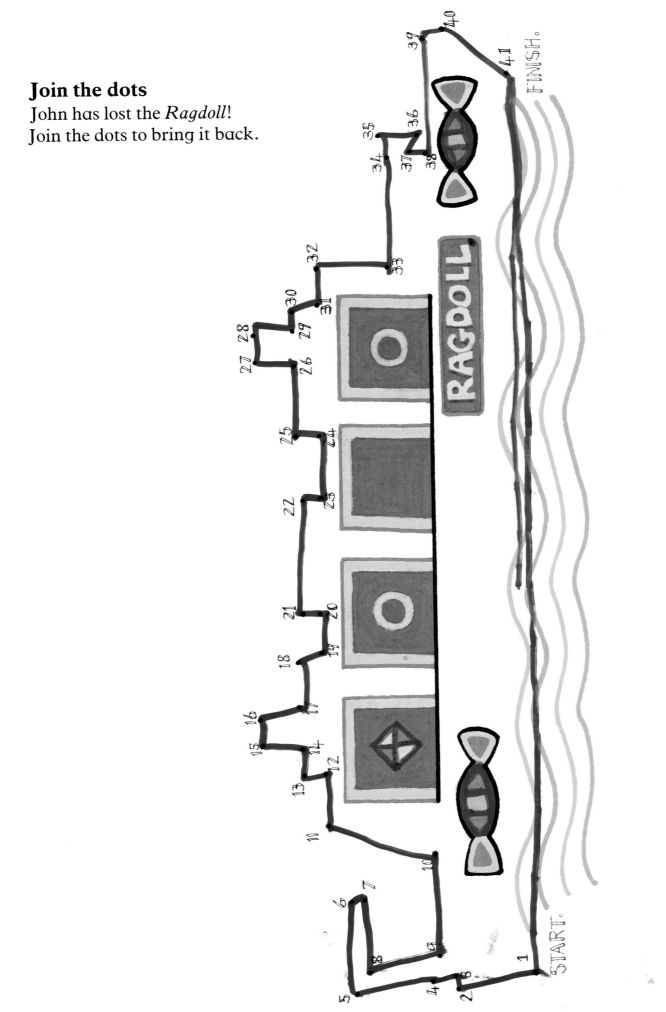

A Walk in Spring

Play this game with Rosie and Jim as they walk through the countryside on the way back to the *Ragdoll*.

You will need a die to throw and a counter for each player. Put all the counters on *START*. Take it in turns to throw the die and move your counter around the board. The first person to reach the *Ragdoll* is the winner.

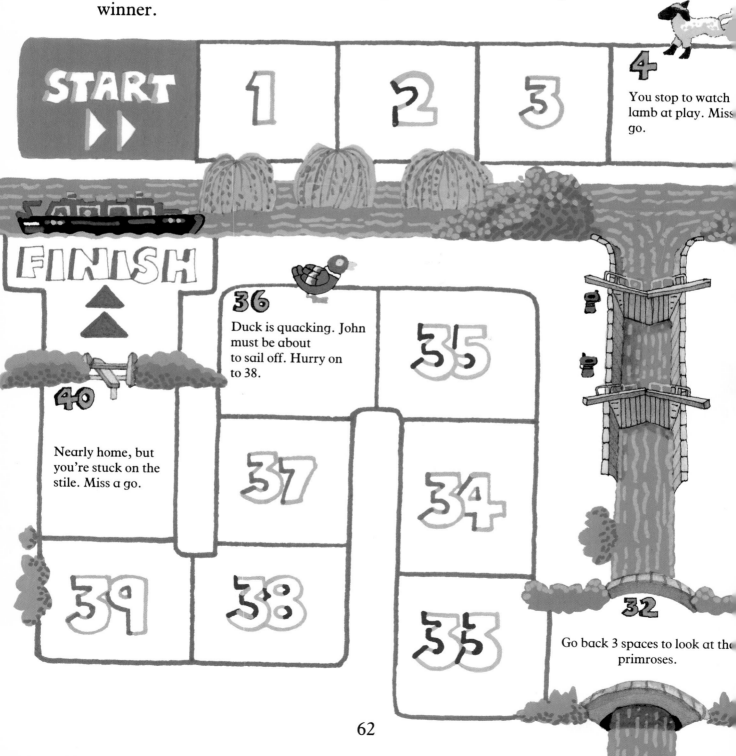

START ▶▶

1

2

3

4 You stop to watch lamb at play. Miss go.

FINISH ▲ ▲

36 Duck is quacking. John must be about to sail off. Hurry on to 38.

35

40 Nearly home, but you're stuck on the stile. Miss a go.

37

34

39

38

33

32 Go back 3 spaces to look at the primroses.

7

8

9

10

11 How many birds are hiding in this tree? Move one space for each bird you count.

6

14

13 You find a baby rabbit. Take it back to its mother at square 8.

12

5

15

16

17 Shelter under a tree from a Spring shower. Throw a 4 to move on.

18

27

26 You run after a butterfly for a closer look. Go to 31.

25

19

28

29

24

20 There's a rainbow! Move forward one space for every colour you count.

30 Find three animals hiding in the hedgerow. Then move on three spaces.

23

22 It's getting quite warm. Stop for a rest and miss a go.

21

31

Answers

Page 43

Page 52

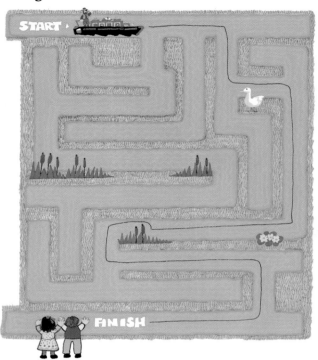

Page 53
Butterfly number 1 is the odd one out.

Calf number 4 is the odd one out.